Peter Rabbit's ABC and 123

With new reproductions from the original illustrations

BY BEATRIX POTTER

F. WARNE & Co

Aa

a is for apples

Red and green apples,
in a big brown pot

b is for butter

Samuel Whiskers is
stealing the butter!

Cc

c is for carrot

This rabbit's mother has
given him a carrot

Dd

d is for duck

Can you make a
noise like a duck?

Ee

e is for egg

A present of an egg
for Mr Brown

f is for fish

Splash! Jack Sharp,
covered in spines

Ff

Gg

g is for gate

Look at naughty Peter Rabbit,
squeezing under the gate

Hh

h is for hedgehog

Mrs Tiggy-winkle
is nothing but a hedgehog!

I i

i is for iron

Mrs Tiggy-winkle ironing,
makes a nice hot singey smell

j is for jacket

Peter Rabbit's jacket,
hanging on the scarecrow

Kk

k is for kitten

Mittens, Tom Kitten and Moppet,
playing in the garden

l is for ladybird

"Fly away home,
Mother Ladybird!"

Mm

m is for mouse

A little mouse, on top
of the cupboard

Nn

n is for newspaper

The foxy-gentleman looks over
the top of his newspaper

Oo

o is for owl

Can you make a noise
like an owl?

P p

p is for pig

This little pig went to market;
his name is Pigling Bland

Qq

q is for quilt

Little baby mice,
sleeping all in a row

Rr

r is for rabbits

Can you see the little
bunny, peeping over?

Ss

s is for strawberry

Timmy Willie eats roots and salad
(and sometimes a strawberry)

Tt

t is for teacup

Simpkin the cat
was fond of mice

Uu

u is for umbrella

Timmy and Goody Tiptoes,
under an umbrella

Vv

v is for violets

Timmy Willie sits in the sun,
sniffing the smell of violets

W w

w is for washing

Mrs Tiggy-winkle,
hanging up her washing

Xx

x is in fox

Jemima Puddle-duck
meets a foxy-gentleman

Y y

y is for yard

Lucie is in the farm-yard,
looking for her pocket-handkins

Zz

z is for "Zzz, bizz"

Can you make a noise
like a bee?

1

one rabbit

How many little rabbits,
eating radishes?

two stockings

How many yellow stockings
for Sally Henny-penny?

3

three kittens

One, two, three little kittens,
playing in the dust

four guinea-pigs

How many guinea-pigs can
you see in the garden?

5

five mice

How many mice sewing,
with scissors and thread?

six rabbits

How many Flopsy Bunnies,
peeping in the window?

7

seven squirrels

Can you count the red squirrels
with the old brown owl?

eight piglets

How many piglets,
feeding from a trough?

9

nine mice

Can you count the mice,
sitting up for supper?

10

ten mice

How many little mice,
living in a shoe?

11

eleven hens

How many hens
in the hen coop?

twelve animals

How many animals
round the notice-board?

FREDERICK WARNE

Published by the Penguin Group
27 Wrights Lane, London W8 5TZ, England
Penguin Books USA Inc., 375 Hudson Street, New York, New York 10014, USA
Penguin Books Australia Ltd, Ringwood, Victoria, Australia
Penguin Books Canada Ltd, 10 Alcorn Avenue, Toronto, Ontario, Canada M4V 3B2
Penguin Books (NZ) Ltd, 182-190 Wairau Road, Auckland 10, New Zealand

Penguin Books Ltd, Registered Offices: Harmondsworth, Middlesex, England

First published 1995 by Frederick Warne
Miniature edition first published 1997
1 3 5 7 9 10 8 6 4 2

Manufactured in China by Imago Publishing Ltd.